How to use this book

Follow the advice, in italics, given for you on each page.
Support the children as they read the text that is shaded in cream.
Praise *the children at every step!*

Detailed guidance is provided in the Read Write Inc. Phonics Handbook.

8 reading activities

Children:
- *Practise reading the speed sounds.*
- *Read the green, red and challenge words for the story.*
- *Listen as you read the introduction.*
- *Discuss the vocabulary check with you.*
- *Read the story.*
- *Re-read the story and discuss the 'questions to talk about'.*
- *Re-read the story with fluency and expression.*
- *Practise reading the speed words.*

Speed sounds

Consonants *Say the pure sounds (do not add 'uh').*

f (ff)	l ll	m (mm)	n nn kn	r rr	s ss ce	v ve	z zz s	sh	th	ng nk

b bb	c k (ck)	d dd	g gg	h	j	p pp	qu	t (tt)	w wh	x	y	ch (tch)

Vowels *Say the vowel sound and then the word, eg 'a', 'at'.*

at	hen head	in	on	up	day	see happy	high	blow

zoo	look	car	for	fair	whirl	shout	boy

*Each box contains one sound but sometimes more than one grapheme. Focus graphemes are **circled**.*

Green words

gr<u>ee</u>n   st<u>ee</u>p   ro<u>ck</u>   o<u>ff</u>   ma<u>tch</u>   <u>th</u>r<u>ee</u>   flo<u>ck</u>   <u>sh</u><u>ee</u>p   cra<u>ck</u>   us

Read in syllables.

a<u>tt</u>' ic → a<u>tt</u>ic   Gran' dad → Grandad

Read the root word first and then with the ending.

s<u>ee</u> → s<u>ee</u>s   trick → tri<u>ck</u>ing

swim → swi<u>mm</u>i<u>ng</u>   sl<u>ee</u>p → sl<u>ee</u>py

Red words

<u>th</u>e   we   to   he   <u>th</u>ey   go   <u>are</u>   of   for*   looks*   good*

* Red word for this book only

5

Vocabulary check

Discuss the meaning (as used in the story) after the children have read the word.

definition:

flock of sheep   *a group of sheep*

Punctuation to note in this story:

Zac Yasmin Grandad	*Capital letters for names*
They At In	*Capital letters that start sentences*
.	*Full stop at the end of each sentence*
!	*Exclamation mark used to show surprise*
...	*Wait and see*

A map in the attic

Introduction

Have you ever followed a map? A map is a picture which tells you which way to go to get somewhere.

In this story Zac and his sister Yasmin find a map in Grandad's attic – it tells them how to reach a big rock. What do you think they will find when they get there? Let's see what happens.

Story written by Cynthia Rider
Illustrated by Tim Archbold

Zac and Yasmin see a green box

in Grandad's attic.

Yasmin peeps in and sees a map.

Zac looks at the map.

"We must get to this big rock," he says.

They set off up a steep hill.

They go past a deep pond with

six ducks swimming on it.

They go past a flock of sleepy sheep.

At last, they see a rock next to three trees.

Yasmin sees a tin in a crack in the rock.

In it are three tickets for next week's match!

"Grandad has been

tricking us!" says Zac.

"But it's a very

good trick, Grandad!"

Questions to talk about

Re-read the page. Read the question to the children. Tell them whether it is a **FIND IT** *question or* **PROVE IT** *question.*

FIND IT	PROVE IT
✓ Turn to the page	✓ Turn to the page
✓ Read the question	✓ Read the question
✓ Find the answer	✓ Find your evidence
	✓ Explain why

Page 8: FIND IT — *What colour is the box in Grandad's attic?*
What does Yasmin spot inside?

Page 9: FIND IT — *Where does Zac think they must get to?*

Page 10-11: FIND IT — *What do they go past?*

Page 12: FIND IT — *What does Yasmin spot? Where is it?*

Page 13: PROVE IT — *Who do you think hid the map in the attic?*
What does Zac think of the surprise?